SERIAL

LiTTLE
EVA
iNK

WRITER AND CREATOR - MITCH BROWN

SERIAL

COVER - MICHAEL GOLDEN
PENCILS - DON THOMAS
COLORS, INKS AND LETTERS - MATTHEW WARLICK
COVER LOGO - NATE PRIDE
CREDITS ART - WILFREDO TORRES
ILLUSTRATIONS FOR "FRIENDLY COMPETITION" -
MICHAEL GOLDEN

LITTLE
EVA
INK

WWW.EVAINK.COM

BONUS SHORT STORY
"FRIENDLY COMPETITION"
INCLUDED!

JACK CONSIDERED PAST CASES.

HAROLD PARKS. HE NEVER CONFESSED TO ONE OF THE KILLINGS. COULD THAT HAVE BEEN MATT?

THIS IS JACK WINTERS. GET THE CHIEF ON THE PHONE, ASAP.

TED KNIGHT'S SHOOTING BY MATT. MATT NEVER EXPLAINED THE NECESSITY FOR THAT SHOOTING.

DID MATT SILENCE THE ONLY MAN WHO COULD HAVE PROVIDED EVIDENCE AGAINST HIM?

IT WAS TIME TO TAKE MATT DOWN.

UNBELIEVABLE!

REEEEOOOOO!

"FRIENDLY COMPETITION"

by Mitch Brown

Neither knew the other's real name. They knew one another by "Victor" and "Marcus." But each knew they were at the top of their profession. Assassins. Hitmen. The best of the best. They charged a million or more a job — because they never failed to deliver.

Victor was a tall, thin man with an olive complexion and a full head of jet black hair. Marcus had more of a stocky build, with pale complexion and thinning red hair. Both exuded confidence, although in different ways. Victor was standoffish, almost snobbish. Marcus was more of an everyman.

They both found it curious they suffered the malady of boredom despite their chosen professions. Each found their marks too easy, even when their employers thought it would be otherwise. To escape the tiresomeness of the easy mark, they had decided to spice up their lives with some friendly challenges. The excitement of their early days in their professions returned in full when they competed with one another.

Once again they met at their favorite restaurant a few blocks from Times

Square. Always the second floor; always the private room. This would be their third dinner meeting — and their third wager.

Their first competition had been to determine which of them — using only bullets or knives — could take out the most Los Angeles gang members in a single month. Victor had won the competition, killing ten, mostly from the populous ranks of the MS-13 gang, while Marcus had only bagged eight. Marcus had paid the freight for their second dinner — the wager between the two men.

Marcus had gotten his revenge in their second competition — killing more mafia members than Victor in one month's time — and Victor was required to buy the dinner being served.

"I noticed you ordered a second bottle of Opus One, Marcus," said Victor with a playful sneer. "Taking advantage of your victory a bit, it seems."

"What can I say? I'm on top," muttered Marcus.

"So what's our next competition, then? Victor asked. "Your time as the winner will be short-lived."

"I've been thinking about it a lot," Marcus said, then hesitated. "I think I've come up with the best competition yet."

"Oh really?" said Victor, curiosity piqued.

Marcus reached into his coat pocket. He pulled out a folded piece of paper and passed it to Victor. Victor's eyebrows rose slightly as he unfolded the paper and saw it was a printed internet page from the FBI's "Wanted" lists.

"This…" said Marcus with dramatic effect, "will truly show which of us is the best. Unlike in our prior contests, these targets are all underground."

Victor stared, steely-eyed, at Marcus. "How many months do you propose?" he asked.

"I propose six months. No budget limitations. As long as the target is on one of the lists, it counts. As always, the winner must show the most verifiable target terminations during the time period."

Victor smiled as he reached his outstretched hand across the table. "Deal."

Marcus returned the smile with a grin. "We meet back here at this restaurant, same time, in exactly six months to celebrate the competition and the winner. Agreed?"

"Agreed," said Victor, as he leaned back in his chair and took another sip of wine.

Five Months and Twenty Eight Days Later, 4pm, New York City

William Wade, Jr. had managed to hide from federal authorities for quite some time. The serial child molester and escaped con from Florida had shaved his head, gotten tattooed from almost head to foot, and moved to New York to try to blend in with the masses. While Wade had succeeded in escaping the authorities, he had done so only barely. Two FBI agents were now following him, posing as tourists with cameras and trailing him down the crowded city streets from a distance. The agents were waiting to nab Wade when he was in less crowded space, as he was considered potentially dangerous. Out of the corner of his eye, Wade had spotted one of the men and began to grow suspicious after the man seemed to be going in his direction for too long to be coincidence. In addition, unbeknownst to Wade, a more dangerous hunter was closing in on him — the world class assassin Marcus.

Marcus knew that Victor had a three to two lead on him. Victor had provided the proof of his successful hits beyond dispute. He had managed to actually kill one of the FBI's "wanted terrorists" in Sudan. 'Truly remarkable,' conceded Marcus.

Marcus had only days to achieve a tie. He had done a lot of work to locate William Wade, and had gotten incredibly lucky in that Wade now resided in New York, his rendezvous point with Victor at their designated restaurant.

Marcus leaned against the brick wall, a copy of the New York Times in his hands. He wore a ball cap and blue jean jacket open over a Yankees T-shirt. He also sported glasses — no prescription. He watched Wade amble down the crowded city street. Wade stopped at a street vendor and handed over a few crumpled dollars for a porn magazine. Wade appeared nervous, frequently looking from side to side, as if he knew someone was tracking him. 'There's no way this moron could have detected *me*,' Marcus thought, as he decided he would pose as a maintenance worker and kill Wade the next morning as Wade emerged from his apartment, unless a better opportunity arose.

Marcus continued shadowing Wade. He just needed to ensure that Wade went home for the night. He would then terminate Wade the next morning, after which he would go have a nice breakfast.

Wade became more and more anxious. Marcus finally allowed himself to wonder, 'Could he have spotted me following him?'

Suddenly, Wade threw the bag containing the porn mag into a wastebasket and took off, walking hurriedly towards a subway station entrance. Alarmed, Marcus did his best to follow inconspicuously.

Marcus hated the thought of losing to that pompous Victor. His stress level rose quickly when Wade boarded a train headed away from the direction of his apartment. It was now 5pm. 'Where in the hell is he going?' thought Marcus. Using all of his years of experience and training, he boarded the same train and continued to observe Wade while remaining unseen. He felt sure Wade had not spotted him. Yet, Wade continued to act apprehensive. Marcus removed his glasses and cap and buttoned his jacket just in case to mix things up.

Wade waited at the stop outside Queens until the train was about to shut its doors and move along, then he abruptly rose from his chair and bolted out of the train. Marcus knew, observing from the adjacent box car, that if Wade got out on the street to a cab, he may not return home and the game would be lost.

Marcus assessed the situation. He knew the time had to be now. He too could easily get to street level at this stop and disappear into the city. He made his decision. He hurled himself out of the train car just as the doors were closing, simultaneously pulling out a hunting knife but obscuring the blade with his jacket sleeve. He rushed toward Wade taking short, quick steps. As if sensing danger, Wade turned towards the approaching killer.

Acting as if he were merely bumping into another train passenger, Marcus stepped in front of Wade and plunged the knife deeply into Wade's chest, twisting the blade. Wade made only a gurgling sound as he crumpled to the floor. The stabbing had been brutally forceful, but quick and almost entirely without sound.   A casual observer would likely think Wade had fainted or collapsed from an illness until they looked closer and saw the pooling blood. Marcus withdrew the knife and in the same motion began his exit for the street silently, looking for a cab. He looked back only once, seeing a tourist bent down over the lifeless body of William Wade. Marcus exited the substation and found a taxi promptly, as he surmised he might, and vanished.

'Victor has not won,' Marcus thought with a smile. He could not wait to tell

Victor the game ended in a draw. 'The expression on Victor's face when I tell him will be priceless,' Marcus mused.

Two Days Later, at the Restaurant

As Marcus entered their reserved room at the restaurant, Victor had already arrived, complete with wolfish smile. Marcus said, "I see you have already ordered the Opus One, Victor" as he seated himself at the table. "Yes, and I've poured us each a glass, my friend," Victor replied.

Victor next snidely announced, "Marcus, as I told you when last we met, your time as the winner would be short-lived. I've won."

"Not so fast, Victor," said Marcus, grinning. "I know you have three scores. However, two days ago, I got my third as well."

"Is that so?" Victor said. The waiter approached the men, interrupted them briefly, and took their orders for appetizers. After the waiter left, Marcus smiled thinly, raised his glass, and savored the wine as he triumphantly told Victor of the details of the murder of William Wade. Victor listened dispassionately, as if stunned.

Finally, after a pregnant pause, Victor said, "A stabbing in the subway right here in the city just *two days* before our deadline. In broad daylight, no less! Impressive, Marcus. Your competitive side is on full display."

Marcus grinned again. "I couldn't let you win a second time, Victor. Now we must consider a different competition."

Victor sat back and looked at his wrist watch. He then leaned forward, one eyebrow arched. "Oh, but I *did* win a second time, Marcus."

Puzzled, Marcus looked at Victor, whose image suddenly began to blur. Marcus rubbed at his eyes gently.

Victor reached into his coat pocket and pulled out a white envelope. He handed it to Marcus.

"Marcus, I must report," Victor said, as he pushed back from the table, "that you have *lost*. *Four* to three. Apparently others — *federal* others with cameras — were also following your William Wade when you killed him. One must have snapped a nice photo of your personage at the scene, as you'll see. I'll leave this dinner for you to pay, although of course that may be pointless now."

Victor rose from the table. "Goodbye, my friend. I do hate that I'll have to stop frequenting this fine establishment."

Victor turned and walked away, and Marcus watched as he left the restaurant. Marcus tried to rise from his chair, but found his body unwilling. He looked at Victor's wine glass. Untouched and full. His vision blurred more. He tried to speak but was unable. He clumsily opened the envelope Victor had handed him, his hands shaking uncontrollably.

As sweat beaded on his forehead, Marcus pulled a printed internet picture from the envelope. He stared at it in disbelief. He knew at once he had been poisoned. He also knew he'd fairly lost the competition to Victor. He begrudgingly respected the smug Victor with his last coherent thoughts. Marcus fell from his chair and collapsed. The printed photo of him — as a "John Doe" on the FBI's "Wanted for Murder" list — fell to the floor with him.

END.

About *"Serial"* and *"Friendly Competition"* from author Mitch Brown ...

Eva Ink: So, tell us how you came up with the ideas for these books, Mitch.

Mitch Brown: The high concepts popped into my head at different times. Once there, the only way to get them out of my brain is to write them down! Of course, there have been a lot of novels, comics, graphic novels and movies on assassins and serial killers. However, I don't think there have been stories with the twists these two tales have. "All is not as it seems" and irony are at work in both stories, and both have plot twists at the end that hopefully the reader appreciates...

Eva Ink: Were the concepts inspired by any other works?

MB: No. I've always loved crime fiction in general and so I suppose generally that could be considered an inspiration.

Eva Ink: How did you like working with the creative team on these stories?

MB: Really enjoyed it. It takes a very long time for a concept for a story to convert from thought inside the brain to graphic depiction on paper. I'm a big fan of *"Serial"* cover artist Michael Golden, who does superb work. Loved his interior illustrations for *"Friendly Competition,"* too. Don Thomas also did a great job and he and Nate Pride and Matthew Warlick are a pleasure to work with.

Eva Ink: Are there any planned follow up stories to either *"Serial"* or *"Friendly Competition"*?

MB: They were both conceived as one shots, so no. *"Friendly Competition"* could lend itself to a pretty cool expanded story, as could *"Serial."*

Eva Ink: Anything else in the works?

MB: I've got two other stories in production, but they are in another genre. I love the graphic novel format. It is true that a "picture is worth a thousand words." I don't have time to try to write novels, so these formats are a great medium for me to get these stories told.

DEMON'S REGRET

Representing painters, writers and illustrators:
Michael Golden, **Steve Scott** *and* **Mark Texeira**!

About *"The Hetairia"* from author Mitch Brown ...

Eva Ink: So, what inspired *"Hetairia?"* It seems a mix of history, religion, science fiction, and superhero genres.

Mitch Brown: It is a mix! I thought about the many Biblical references to "giants" and figured, would there possibly be the remains of any of that race of giants out there? Then, I considered modern advances in cloning and the like and put those concepts together and got the idea of what if the giants of old could be reborn through modern science? And what if the intent of their rebirth was to further evil? I then needed some heroic force to combat the evil giants and the group that created them, and thus conceived of the *"Hetairia"* which has several meanings, one of which is "secret society." The "Hetairia" is a secret sub-group of all of the most famous historical orders of knights, which themselves are shrouded in mystery in many ways.

Eva Ink: How did you like working with the artists on this one?

MB: It was great. I really dug the cover by James. Don Thomas also did a great job with the interior art. Nate Pride and Matthew Warlick were again a pleasure to work with.

Eva Ink: Are there any planned follow up stories for the *"Hetairia?"*

MB: There certainly could be both prequels and sequels. The *"Hetairia"* has, as can be seen in the story, existed as an ongoing group for many decades and would have faced other menaces in the distant past and will face more dangers in the future.

Eva Ink: I know you have also written a mini-series entitled *"Demon's Regret,"* which draws from the Bible in part. Are there other stories you have in the works that are similar?

MB: Not at this time, but folks are fascinated with religion and there are really good stories that are in the Bible, not to mention stories that can emanate from the Bible.

ACRE. NEAR THE END OF THE CRUSADES.

THE TEUTONIC KNIGHTS CONTROLLED IMPORTANT PORTS NEAR THE END OF THE CRUSADES.

AFTER THE CRUSADES, THE TEUTONIC KNIGHTS MOVED INTO HUNGARY, THEN PRUSSIA, THEN POLAND.

ORDERED DISSOLVED IN 1809 BY NAPOLEON BONAPARTE, THE TEUTONIC KNIGHTS AS A FIGHTING FORCE DISAPPEARED.

THOUGH FEW IN THEIR NUMBER, HOWEVER, THOSE WHO BELONGED TO THE HETAIRIA ENDURED.

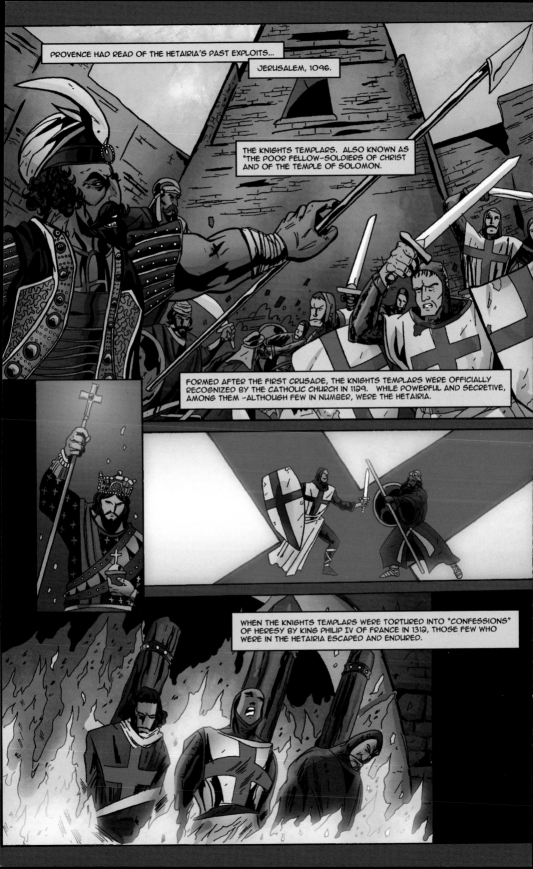

HE HADN'T BEEN SPOTTED - THAT WAS GOOD. PROVENCE WAS READY TO GET SOME REST BEFORE HEADING BACK TO THE COMPOUND AT MALTA.

THERE WERE FEW OF THEM RIGHT NOW - THE HETAIRIA. AS ONE GOT TOO OLD FOR MEMBERSHIP, HE WOULD RETIRE, SWEARING AN OATH OF SILENCE TO HIS DEATH.

ALL WERE CELIBATE. ALL WERE FIGHTERS. ALL WERE WEAPON-MASTERS. ALL WERE CRACK MARKSMEN. ALL WERE SCHOLARS. AND ALL WERE MEN OF GOD.

PROVENCE DID NOT GET TO WATCH MUCH TELEVISION. THAT WAS AN EXTRA TREAT HE GOT WHEN HE WENT ON A MISSION LIKE THIS. THE FOOTBALL GAME WOULD BE ENJOYABLE.

PREPARATION. LEARNING. PRACTICING. PRAYING. PROVENCE HAD BEEN DOING IT FOR YEARS. NEVER HAD THE HETAIRIA BEEN REQUIRED TO SHOW ITSELF IN FORCE TO HIS MEMORY.

THINGS WERE ABOUT TO CHANGE.

METROPOLITAN MUSEUM OF ART, NEW YORK CITY.

RAYMOND PROVENCE HAD BEEN SENT TO SEE IF THE BONES REALLY WERE AUTHENTIC MISSING BONES OF ST. WINIFRED STOLEN FROM A RELIQUARY.

IT HAD TAKEN ONLY A MOMENT FOR RAYMOND TO DETERMINE, USING THE AURA SURROUNDING THE REAL RELIC IN HIS HAND - THE PRAYER STONE OF A PEASANT MARTYR HAVING TRUE SUPERNATURAL POWERS - THAT ST. WINIFRED'S BONES WERE NOT IN THE GLASS CASE.

THAT'S 4 FAKES IN A ROW I'VE FOUND. CURATORS THESE DAYS DON'T KNOW THEIR STUFF. BACK ON A PLANE TO MALTA IN THE MORNING.

PROVENCE WAS A MEMBER OF A SMALL, SECRET, AND VERY ELITE GROUP - THE HETAIRIA. THE GROUP WAS THOUSANDS OF YEARS OLD - THEIR EXISTENCE MAINTAINED ONLY TO PROTECT TRUE RELICS AND TO STAND AGAINST ANY TRUE THREAT TO THE FAITH.

TWO OF HIS COLLEAGUES, JAMES FERDINAND AND SEBASTIAN BALDWIN, WERE ON OTHER MISSIONS IN THE CITY.

BACK OUTSIDE THE MUSEUM, PROVENCE SAW THE GANG OF MEN HARRASSING THE WOMAN IMMEDIATELY. HE WOULD NEED TO MOVE QUICKLY.

YEARS LATER. 45 MILES NORTH OF NEW YORK CITY.

THE SECLUDED LABORATORY COMPOUND OF DR. JONATHAN DRAKE.

EXCELLENT WORK, EVERYONE.

THE CLONING, IN VITRO FERTILIZATION AND IMPREGNATION PROCESS WILL BEGIN TOMORROW.

IS EVERYTHING PREPARED?

FRANKLIN JOHNSON AND DR. JONATHAN DRAKE WERE MEMBERS OF A SHADOWY ORGANIZATION KNOWN TO FEW AS "WELTENDE," OR "WORLD'S END."

DEDICATED TO THE DOMINANCE OVER AND ULTIMATE DESTRUCTION OF HUMANITY, THE GROUP HAD LONG AWAITED THE CHANCE TO USE MODERN SCIENCE TO RESURRECT THE DESTRUCIVE AND EVIL POWER OF THE REPHAIM.

YES, EVERYTHING IS READY.

THE WOMEN ARE READY FOR IMPLANTA-TION AS WELL.

FRANKLIN JOHNSON HAD INDEED BROUGHT THE REMAINS OF THE REPHAIM.

AND NOW, DR. JOHNATHAN DRAKE HAD SUCCESSFULLY EXTRACTED THE DNA FROM THOSE REMAINS.

ALL IS PROCEEDING AS PLANNED.

GOLAN HEIGHTS.

DIG, MEN. DIG!

THE OLD TEXTS TALK OF GIANTS LIVING HERE, INCLUDING KING OG OF BASHAN.

BUT IF WE FIND A BONE FRAGMENT HOW WILL WE KNOW IT CAME FROM ONE OF THE NEPHILIM OR REPHAIM?

JUST DO AS YOU ARE TOLD. BRING ME ANY BONE FRAGMENTS.

THE REPHAIM.

MENTIONED NUMEROUS TIMES IN THE HOLY BIBLE, THEY WERE THE EVIL GIANTS OF OLD.

THE REMAINS OF THE REPHAIM WOULD BE SOMEWHERE. THE BIBLICAL TEXTS WERE HISTORICALLY ACCURATE.

THE GREAT FLOOD WAS A STEP GOD NEEDED TO TAKE TO VIRTUALLY WIPE OUT THIS RACE OF GIANTS, WHO WERE UNHOLY AND EVIL.

GENESIS 6: 5-7

"And it came to pass, when men began to multiply on the face of the earth, and daughters were born unto them, That the sons of God saw the daughters of men that they were fair; and they took them wives of all which they chose. And the Lord said, My spirit shall not always strive with man, for that he also is flesh: yet his days shall be an hundred and twenty years.

There were giants in the earth in those days; and also after that, when the sons of God came in unto the daughters of men, and they bare children to them, the same became mighty men which were of old, men of renown."

Genesis 6: 1-4.

THE KNIGHTS TEMPLAR. THE TEUTONIC KNIGHTS. THE KNIGHTS HOSPITALLER. SHROUDED IN SECRECY AND ABOVE THE LAWS OF SECULAR STATES, THESE KNIGHTS PLAYED CRITICAL ROLES IN DEFENDING CHRISTENDOM BEFORE FADING INTO HISTORY.

WITHIN THESE MILITARY ORDERS LAY AN EVEN MORE ELITE GROUP -- "THE HETAIRIA" OR "SECRET SOCIETY."

THE HETAIRIA DWELT INSIDE THEIR RESPECTIVE ORDERS, COMMUNICATING ONLY WHEN NECESSARY AND SWEARING AN OATH TO ENDURE AND TO TAKE UP THE IMPLEMENTS OF BATTLE AGAIN IN THE FUTURE -- SHOULD THE FAITH BE FACED WITH A THREAT THAT WARRANTED THEIR SPECIAL SKILLS AND KNOWLEDGE.

NOW, JUST SUCH A THREAT HAS EMERGED....

THE HETAIRIA

CREATOR/WRITER

Mitch BROWN

PENCILS

Don THOMAS

INKS

James HARGETT

COLORS & LETTERS

Matthew WARLICK

COVER ARTIST

James HARGETT

TITLE ART BY **WILFREDO TORRES**